Hear Me

Amy Olson

SCHOLASTIC INC.
**New York Toronto London Auckland Sydney
Mexico City New Delhi Hong Kong Buenos Aires**

Illustrations
Nathan Fox

No part of this publication may be reproduced in whole or in part, or stored in a retrieval
system, or transmitted in any form or by any means, electronic, mechanical, photocopying,
recording, or otherwise, without written permission of the publisher. For information
regarding permission, write to Scholastic Inc., 557 Broadway, New York, NY 10012.

Copyright © 2005 by Scholastic Inc.
All rights reserved. Published by Scholastic Inc.
Printed in the U.S.A.

ISBN 0-439-12403-4
(meets NASTA specifications)

SCHOLASTIC, READ 180, and associated logos and designs are
trademarks and/or registered trademarks of Scholastic Inc.

LEXILE is a registered trademark of MetaMetrics, Inc.

17 18 19 20   113   18 17 16 15

Contents

1 Unhappy Signs 4

2 Late for Dinner 10

3 The Big Decision 15

4 Finding the Way 19

5 Learning to Hear 23

American Manual Alphabet 31

Glossary 32

Tina wants to talk with her dad. But he doesn't speak her language.

1 Unhappy Signs

My name is Tina McKinley. I'm 13 and I have a story to tell. I can't tell it by speaking. I don't speak very well. I'm deaf, and it's hard to learn to speak if you can't hear.

I could tell my story really well in **sign language**. But maybe you don't know sign language. My father didn't either, and that's where my story starts.

I was sitting at Ms. Anico's picnic table in her backyard. I love it back there. There's always a cool breeze. In the spring the smells are wonderful. There are apple blossoms and tulips and daisies. It's

I was sitting with Ms. Anico at her picnic table. I love it there.

beautiful. It's not like my house at all.

Ms. Anico is a sign-language teacher. She's also an **interpreter**. She stays with me in school and signs what the teacher is saying. I really don't know what I'd do without her.

Ms. Anico was teaching me some new signs. But I wasn't paying attention.

"Hey, Tina," she signed. "I'm trying to teach you some new words here!"

"Sorry," I signed back.

"What's the matter? You seem upset."

I frowned.

"Is it your father again?" Ms. Anico signed.

I didn't want to talk about it. But she didn't give up.

"He still won't try to sign?" she signed.

"No," I answered.

"That's not right, Tina," she signed. "You know that, don't you?"

I tried to stick up for my father. "It's hard

for him," I signed. "Since Mom died, he's had to work two jobs. He doesn't have time to learn. He's always tired."

"Mr. Anico and I were busy, too," Ms. Anico signed back. "We didn't have much money. But when we found out our son was deaf, we learned to sign. There was never any question."

Ms. Anico reached for my arm. I could feel myself start to cry. I hate it when that happens. My father calls me a baby whenever I cry. I've gotten good at holding back tears. But I couldn't this time. Before I knew it, I was sobbing and signing.

"My dad is always mad at me," I told Ms. Anico. "I don't understand why. I do well in school. I don't get in trouble. But he still gets angry."

I kept signing, "Now Dad gets mad when I sign with my brother and sister. He won't look at me when he talks, so I can't read his lips. I can see that he's mad, but I can't figure out why. Then he tells Kaylyn and Jonah to stop signing to me. And I feel totally alone."

I was a complete mess. I didn't know I had so many tears in me. Ms. Anico moved closer. She held my hands tight. We didn't talk for a long time.

Then Ms. Anico signed, "Tina, you could come live with my family. We all love you. You are welcome here."

I stopped sobbing and looked at Ms. Anico. Then I looked at the apple tree and the flower garden. *This could be my home?* I thought. *I could live with people who understand me? What could be better?*

Then I thought about my brother and sister. And I thought about my father. I hung my head. "It would never work," I signed. "I'd miss Kaylyn and Jonah. Jonah is just eight. I couldn't leave him."

"Tina, Kaylyn is 16," Ms. Anico reminded me. "She can help take care of

Jonah. Think about it."

"My dad would never let me," I signed.

"There might be a way to work it out," Ms. Anico signed.

I didn't know what she meant, and I didn't ask. I packed up my backpack. I took a deep breath of apple-blossom air. And I left to walk home.

Have you ever been with people who didn't understand your language? How did you feel?

Tina's dad is yelling at her. But she has no idea what he's saying.

2 Late for Dinner

It was such a beautiful day. I went the long way through the park. That way I could walk by the lake. It would take longer to get home, and that was fine with me.

I saw a flock of geese playing. They looked so cute. I sat down to watch. They were moving all together, like in a dance. It was like they knew exactly where to go.

They must have been talking to each other. Or maybe they had their own sign language. I wasn't sure how they did it. But they all seemed to understand each other. They were like a big family.

Then I looked at my watch. It was past

dinnertime! My father is very strict about being home for dinner. He was going to be furious. I grabbed my bag and ran all the way home.

When I got there, everyone was sitting at the table. They had finished eating. My father stood up when he saw me.

"Where have you been, Tina?" I could tell he was yelling. "I've been pounding nails all day. Soon I have to go clean floors. I work hard to put food on the table. All I ask is that you be home to eat it. Now I'll have to warm up your food. I don't have time for this!"

I wanted to say I could do it myself. But there was no way to make my father understand. He grabbed my plate and stomped into the kitchen. I could tell he was shouting at me. Kaylyn and Jonah were listening, but I couldn't see him. I had no idea what he was saying.

Then my father came back. He slammed

my plate in front of me. Some pasta sauce spilled on my shirt. I looked up.

"—you?" I only got the last word. "Well? I asked you a question," my father said. "Answer me!"

I didn't know what to say. I was so scared and confused. I looked at Kaylyn. She started to sign to me. But my father interrupted.

"Kaylyn, stop it now! Do not sign in this house! Tina can write down her answer!" He found a pen and paper and shoved it at me.

"Answer me!" he yelled again.

I tried to write, "I don't know what you said." I was shaking and it came out wobbly. I handed it to my father.

He grabbed the paper. "Well that's too bad!" he said. He crumpled the note and threw it on the floor. "You should pay attention."

My father turned away from me.

My father slammed my plate of pasta down on the table.

"Kaylyn, Jonah, go do your homework. Tina can eat alone. I'm going to work."

My father left. I looked at my plate. I didn't feel hungry at all. I felt the tears coming again. This time I stopped them. I thought about Ms. Anico's garden. Then I ran to my room. I picked up my diary and started to write.

What do you think Tina wrote in her diary?

Tina wants to live with Ms. Anico. But what will Tina's father say?

3 The Big Decision

I never show anyone my diary. Now I had a real reason not to. For three days, I carried it with me everywhere. It had my plans inside. I knew what I wanted. But I wasn't brave enough to tell my father yet.

On the third day, my father didn't come home. That happens now and then. Sometimes, he doesn't have time to come home between jobs. There's usually food in the house. So we take care of ourselves.

But that night, there was nothing worth eating. I took five dollars from my savings. It was enough to buy some peanut butter and bread.

I had to know if Ms. Anico would really let me live at her house.

When I got up the next morning, my father was home. But he was asleep. That day at school I decided to ask Ms. Anico a question. It wasn't about schoolwork.

"Were you serious?" I signed. The teacher was talking.

"Be quiet," Ms. Anico signed.

I kept signing. "I need to know. Were you serious about me living with you?"

Ms. Anico stopped signing the teacher's words. She looked over at me. "Of course I was," she answered.

That night, I waited until Kaylyn and Jonah were in bed. I tore a page out of my diary. I wrote my father a letter. Then I put it on the kitchen table.

Here's what the letter said.

Dear Daddy,

I'm sorry I was late for dinner. But I don't think that's why you were mad at me. I think you were mad at me because I am deaf.

I wish you could see that sign language is like any language. I don't speak your language. I'll probably never learn it. You could learn my language. But you won't. Instead, you just get angry.

I've made a decision. Ms. Anico says I could live with her. I want to do it, and I hope you'll let me go. Her whole family knows sign language. I think I'll be much happier there. Maybe when I'm gone, you will be happier, too.

I love you, Daddy. Please try to understand.

Tina

What made Tina decide to leave her father the note?

Tina's father says she can't leave. But Ms. Anico has an idea.

4 Finding the Way

I didn't have to wait long. I got my answer the next morning. Dad was sitting at the table. He had his head in his hands. The note was torn up on the floor.

This time, he looked right at me. He wanted to make sure I understood. "No!" he said. "Do you hear me?! This is your family. Your mother may be gone. But we're still a family. I work hard to give you a good life. And this is how you thank me? The answer is no!"

I just stood there.

"Can't you hear me?!" He banged his fist on the table. "What's wrong with you?!"

The tears started to come. I grabbed my books and ran out the door.

Now I had done it. What was I thinking? Now my father hated me even more. And I had to stay.

The tears started to come. I grabbed my books and ran out the door.

I didn't know where I was going. I just started walking. Soon, Kaylyn and Jonah caught up with me.

"What's going on?" Kaylyn signed. "You can't leave us, Tina."

"That's right," I answered. "I can't. Dad made that perfectly clear."

"Look, Tina, things aren't that bad," Kaylyn continued. "You've got us. And we'd miss you if you left."

Jonah was looking up at me like a puppy. He looked confused and sad. I couldn't look at him any longer.

"I have to go," I signed. I turned and walked away.

Then I realized where I was going. I was going to Ms. Anico's house. "There might be a way," she had said. Maybe there was.

I got there as she was leaving for school. We walked together. I told her about my dad not coming home. I told her about the letter. I told her about him getting so mad.

She had to stop me at the street corners. "Watch for cars, Tina. The story can wait."

"What am I going to do?" I signed, finally. "I made up my mind. He won't let me go. It's going to be worse than ever now."

Ms. Anico opened the door to school. "I talked to a lawyer," she signed. "It won't be easy. It won't be fun. But if you want to, we can go to court. We can ask a judge if you can live with me."

Do you think Tina will go to court? Why or why not?

Tina goes to court. Will her father finally understand her?

5 Learning to Hear

It took me a while to think it all through. I'd have to tell a judge everything. I'd tell about my father getting mad. I'd tell about him not coming home. I'd tell about him not learning sign language.

The judge would decide if I could leave or not. It seemed awful at first. It was like saying my father was a criminal.

Ms. Anico said no, that wasn't it. Being a father was like having a job. Like any job, it takes skills. When your daughter is deaf, it takes extra skills. My father didn't have the skills, she said. He just wasn't doing the job well enough.

So, we went to a judge. Our lawyer told her that I wanted to live with Ms. Anico. The judge set a date for a **hearing**.

I went home to live. It was up and down. Sometimes Dad would come home with ice cream. He'd be really nice. Other times he was worse than ever.

Finally, three months later, we were sitting in court. I was next to Ms. Anico. She squeezed my hand. "You've been very brave," she signed.

I looked over at my father. He was staring straight ahead. He looked lost.

Just then, the judge came in. She walked to her desk.

"All rise," called the **bailiff**. Ms. Anico could have signed it all for me. But the court had a special interpreter.

We all stood up.

"Mr. McKinley," the judge said. "Do you see the sign-language interpreter?"

"Yes, your honor," he answered.

After three months, Ms. Anico, my father, and I were finally in court.

"She is there because the law says she must be there," the judge said. "She is there because Tina doesn't speak our language. What if she could hear but could only speak Spanish? Then I'd have a Spanish language interpreter for her. Do you understand?"

"Yes, your honor," my father answered.

"In the courtroom, we need to communicate with Tina," the judge said. "She deserves the same in her home. But you won't learn sign language."

The judge paused. "You're not home much, Mr. McKinley. When you are, you're hard to live with. That's tough on all your children."

She continued. "It's toughest on Tina. You refuse to sign with her. She's living in silence. She deserves better. I have decided that Marisol Anico will become the **guardian** of Tina McKinley."

The judge banged her **gavel** on the desk hard. I could feel it in my feet.

I couldn't believe it. I had so many feelings at once. I hugged Ms. Anico. Then I looked at my father. I was scared. But I made myself go over to him.

"I can't believe this," my father said. He was looking right at me. He didn't look angry. He just looked sad. I walked over and gave him a hug. I had something I wanted to tell him. So I signed it. Then I walked back to Ms. Anico.

"Wait!" My father came after me. He was shouting at Ms. Anico. "What did she say?! What did she say?!"

"Do you want me to tell him?" Ms. Anico signed to me.

I signed yes.

"Do you really want to know?" she asked my father. He nodded. "Then come to my house twice a week. I'll teach you sign language. You can learn to talk to Tina."

My father opened his mouth. I could tell he wanted to make an excuse. But nothing

"You can learn to talk to your daughter," Ms. Anico told my father.

would come out.

Finally, my father just said, "Okay." His mouth barely moved. But I could tell that's what he said. I could tell because there were tears in his eyes. He was about to cry.

Ms. Anico touched him on the shoulder. "This is your chance. You can get to know your daughter."

"Will you tell me what she said?" my father begged.

Ms. Anico said, "Tina said, 'I hope you will learn to hear me.' And, 'I love you.'"

Do you think Tina's father will learn to sign? Why or why not?

Editor's Note

Tina's story didn't really happen. But it's based on the true story of a 15-year-old named Sonya Kinney. Sonya was deaf. Her father drank heavily and didn't take very good care of his kids. And like Tina's father, Sonya's dad would not learn sign language. In 1995, Sonya took him to court. She won the right to leave home and live with her sign-language teacher.

American Manual Alphabet

To get a feel for signing, you can start with the basics. Here's the alphabet in sign.

Glossary

bailiff *(noun)* someone who helps the judge keep order in a courtroom

gavel *(noun)* a small wooden hammer used to call for quiet in a courtroom

guardian *(noun)* someone who is not the parent of a child but who has the legal responsibility to take care of him or her

hearing *(noun)* a time in court when lawyers and witnesses give information to a judge about a case

interpreter *(noun)* someone who explains what someone is saying in another language

sign language *(noun)* a group of hand signals and movements that deaf people use to communicate